# It's another Quality Book from CGP

*This book has been carefully written for Year 4 children learning science. It's full of questions and investigations designed to cover the Year 4 objectives on 'Animals, including humans' from the latest National Curriculum.*

*There's also plenty of practice at 'Working Scientifically' throughout the book.*

# What CGP is all about

*Our sole aim here at CGP is to produce the highest quality books — carefully written, immaculately presented and dangerously close to being funny.*

*Then we work our socks off to get them out to you — at the cheapest possible prices.*

# Contents

**Answers to the questions are on the back of the Pull-out Poster in the centre of the book.**

Published by CGP

*Contributors*

Katie Braid, Sophie Scott

With thanks to Jill Cousner, Rachel Kordan and Chris Lindle for the proofreading.

ISBN: 978 1 78294 084 5

Clipart from Corel®

Printed by Elanders Ltd, Newcastle upon Tyne.

Based on the classic CGP style created by Richard Parsons.

Text, design, layout and original illustrations © Coordination Group Publications Ltd. (CGP) 2014

All rights reserved.

**Photocopying this book is not permitted, even if you have a CLA licence.**

**Extra copies are available from CGP with next day delivery  •  0800 1712 712  •  www.cgpbooks.co.uk**

## Parts of the Digestive System

*The <u>digestive system</u> is made up of the parts of our body that <u>take in</u> and <u>break down food</u> so it can be used. It's made of lots of <u>different parts</u>.*

1. Use the words below to **label** the picture of the digestive system.

stomach        mouth        large intestine        tongue        oesophagus        small intestine

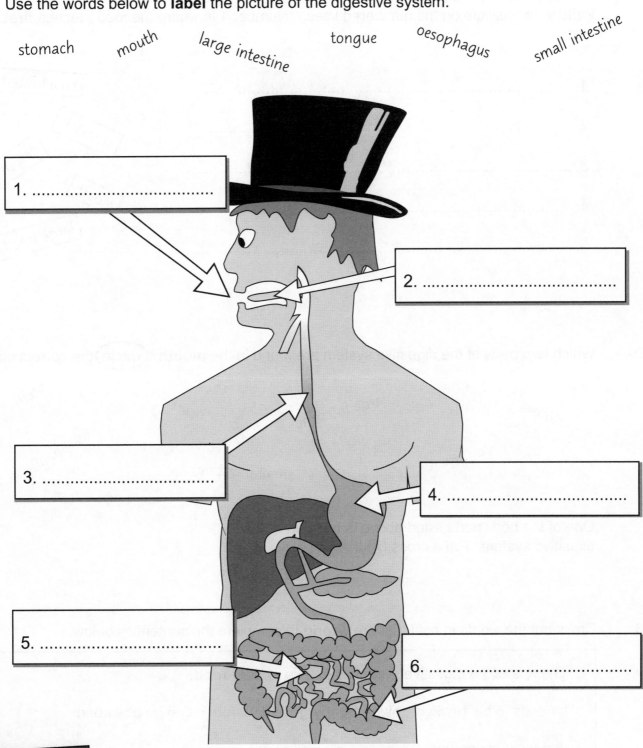

1. ................................

2. ................................

3. ................................

4. ................................

5. ................................

6. ................................

**INVESTIGATE**

• *Get a plain T-shirt that you can draw on. Using a permanent pen, draw on the different
parts of the digestive system (but not the tongue and the mouth). Use Q1 above to help
you. Put the T-shirt on and have a look — did you get everything in the right places?*

# Digesting Food

*Food enters the digestive system at the <u>mouth</u>, which contains the <u>teeth</u> and the <u>tongue</u>.*
*Food travels down the <u>oesophagus</u> to the <u>stomach</u>, <u>small intestine</u> and <u>large intestine</u>.*

1.  Put the parts of the digestive system below in the **order** that food reaches them.
    Write your answers on the numbered lines. (Number 1 is where the food reaches **first**.)

    1. ...............................................................................

    2. ...............................................................................

    3. ...............................................................................

    4. ...............................................................................

    5. ...............................................................................

    small intestine

    stomach

    oesophagus

    mouth

    large intestine

2.  Which **two** parts of the digestive system are found in the **mouth**? (Circle) the correct ones.

    stomach        large intestine        heart        teeth

    tongue                        small intestine        oesophagus

    One of the body parts listed above is **not** part of the
    digestive system. Put a cross (✗) through it.

3.  Cross out the words in bold that are **wrong** to complete the sentences below.

    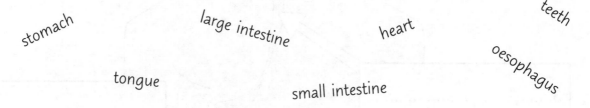

    The role of the digestive system is to take in **air / food**.

    It needs to be **broken down / lightly grilled** before it can be absorbed

    and used by the body.

    The first place the food will reach is the **mouth / stomach** where the

    **teeth / oesophagus** can chew the food to break it up into **larger / smaller** pieces.

    © CGP — not to be photocopied

# Digesting Food

4. Draw lines to match the **parts** of the digestive system on the left with their **functions** on the right.

*'Function' is just a fancy word for job. The function of something is what it does.*

PARTS

Oesophagus

Mouth

Small intestine

Stomach

Large intestine

FUNCTIONS

Transports food to the stomach.

Absorbs water into the body.

Breaks down food into tiny bits which are then absorbed into the body.

Churns up food which helps to break it down.

Contains the teeth and tongue which chew and break up food.

5. Put **arrows** in the boxes on the picture on the right to show the **direction** that food moves through the digestive system.

Draw an arrow pointing to the part of the body where food is absorbed into the blood. Label this part **A**.

*Saying something is absorbed is another way of saying something is taken in.*

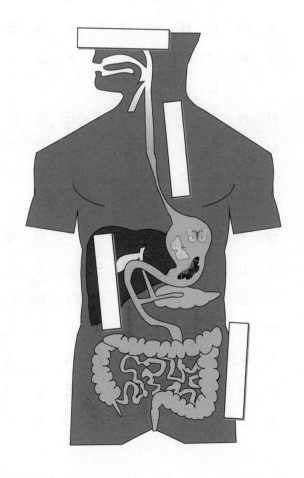

# Digesting Food

6.   Why is it important for food to be **broken down** in the digestive system?
Choose the correct answer and write it on the dotted lines below.

The food needs to be in small pieces so that it can be taken into the body and bloodstream.

Food tastes better when it is broken down into little pieces.

The food won't fit through the oesophagus unless it is in tiny pieces.

.................................................................................................................

.................................................................................................................

7.   See if you can **find** all the parts of the digestive system in the word search below.

```
T A B F Q U A L E R T M A Q F
V O B R H U B A R E P O L L P
C A N R H O R R S N E I N D Y
Y I L G U L E G L I J A M U T
U H A X U O E E S T O M A C H
M I A V L E S I R S G S B V Q
Y C G P T S S N T E A P E E C
U N A E O O C T S T A J T Q U
M I C H E P I E N N E A E P P
Y L E N O H E S L I G R E A P
U E F L A A O T E L R J T I N
M N G L E G B I E L L R H O C
L K M O D U A N T A Y B P A Q
V B X G G S A E E M B L S T O
M O U T H A C H I S N T E S T
```

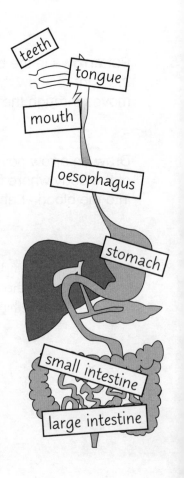

teeth

tongue

mouth

oesophagus

stomach

small intestine

large intestine

          © CGP — not to be photocopied

# Digesting Food

8.  **Label** the parts of the digestive system shown below.
    Write the correct name on the dotted line.

 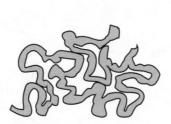  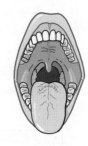

.......................     .......................     .......................     .......................

.......................     .......................     .......................     .......................

9.  Where is **food** absorbed into the bloodstream?

    ....................................................................................................

10. Where is **water** absorbed into the body?

    ....................................................................................................

11. Fill in the gaps below to complete the sentences about the
    **digestive system**.  Use the words from the mouth on the right.

    Food enters the digestive system at the ............................... .

    Our teeth help to break the food up into ............................... pieces

    by chewing.

    Our tongue helps us to chew and ............................... .

    The ............................... is the pipe that transports food to our

    stomach.  In the stomach, food is ................................... to help

    break it down.

churned up

smaller

oesophagus

swallow

mouth

---

**INVESTIGATE**  · · · · · · · · · · · · · · · · · · · · · · · · · · · · · · · · ·

- *Write a short story to describe the journey of a sandwich as it moves through the digestive*
  *system, from the mouth to the bloodstream.  Think about the job of each part of the*
  *digestive system and what would happen to the sandwich in each part.  Lovely thoughts...*

© CGP — not to be photocopied

# Section 2 — Teeth

## Your Teeth

*Teeth help us <u>crush</u>, <u>tear</u> and <u>bite</u>. They are <u>hard</u> and <u>strong</u> so they can break up all sorts of food. Teeth are <u>held in place</u> by the <u>gums</u>.*

1. Complete the sentences using the words from the thought bubble.

break   hard
eat   pink
white   hold   gums

Teeth are ..............................

and very .............................. .

They are used to

.............................. up

food and they help us to

.............................. .

These are the .............................. .

They are soft and

.............................. . They

help to ..............................

the teeth in place.

2. Some of your teeth have probably fallen out. But they will be replaced by bigger, better adult teeth. On the picture below, **colour in** any of your teeth which have **fallen out**.

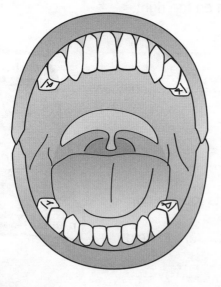

3. What is the name given to your first set of teeth?

..............................................

### INVESTIGATE ..................................

- *Draw a tally chart with two columns and seven rows. In the first column write 'Number of teeth lost' and then write '0', '1', '2', '3', '4', and '5 or more' in the rows beneath this. In the second column write 'Number of people'. Ask your classmates how many teeth they have lost. Which is the most common category? Which category do you fit into?*

*Section 2 — Teeth*

© CGP — not to be photocopied

# Shapes of Teeth

*We have <u>three</u> different types of teeth — <u>canines</u>, <u>incisors</u> and <u>molars</u>.*
*They are <u>different shapes</u> as they have <u>different jobs</u>.*

1.  Below are the letters that make up the names of 3 types of teeth.
    **Unscramble** the letters and write the name on the dotted line.

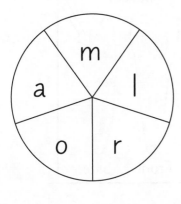 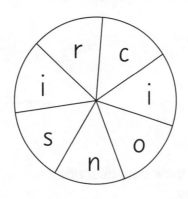 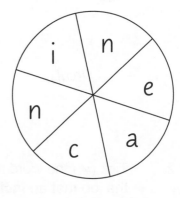

..............................        ..............................        ..............................

2.  Look in your mouth — you will see **three** different shapes of teeth.
    Draw the three **shapes** (one in each box) and **count** how many of each are in your mouth.

| How many of this type of tooth do you have... | How many of this type of tooth do you have... | How many of this type of tooth do you have... |
|---|---|---|
| in your bottom jaw? ☐ | in your bottom jaw? ☐ | in your bottom jaw? ☐ |
| in your top jaw? ☐ | in your top jaw? ☐ | in your top jaw? ☐ |

**INVESTIGATE**

· *Draw a picture of a mouth with all the adult teeth — that's 20 molars, 4 canines and*
· *8 incisors. Make sure you draw them in the right place on both the top and bottom jaws.*
· *Label all of the different teeth. Grab a mirror and give us a grin if you're struggling.*

© CGP — not to be photocopied        *Section 2 — Teeth*

# Different Types of Teeth

*Our teeth have different jobs. Incisors are good for <u>cutting</u>, canines
are good for <u>tearing</u> and molars are good for <u>grinding</u>.*

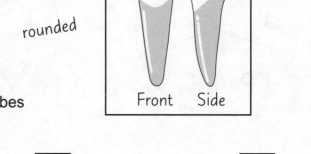

*This is the bit of tooth you can see.
The grey bit is called the <u>root</u> and is
buried in the gum.*

1.  On the right is a picture of a tooth called an **incisor**.
    (Circle) the words that describe the **shape of an incisor**.

blunt

sharp

circular

flat-edged

rounded

**Incisor**

Front    Side

2.  Tick (✔) the word that you think best describes
    the job that an **incisor** does.

    grinding ☐          cutting ☐          sucking ☐

3.  On the right is a picture of a tooth called a **canine**.
    (Circle) the correct words in the sentences
    below to describe their **shape** and **job**.

    Canines are **long / short** and **blunt / pointy**.

    This makes them good for **gripping / swallowing** food.

    Canines also help **tear / grind** food into

    smaller pieces.

    Canines are found at the **front / back** of the mouth.

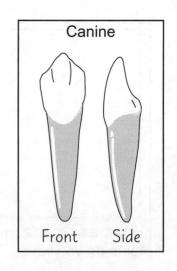

**Canine**

Front    Side

4.  **Molars** are the big teeth at the back of your mouth.
    (Circle) the correct words to explain **what molars do**.

    Molars are **big / small** teeth at the **front / back** of the mouth.

    They have a **bumpy / smooth** surface.

    They are used for **biting / grinding** food.

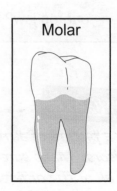

**Molar**

                    © CGP — not to be photocopied

# Different Types of Teeth

5.  Wolves and sheep have different diets and different teeth.
    Read these sentences then fill in the missing **tooth** names below.

Molars can crack and crush bones. They are good for grinding up food.

Incisors are good for cutting through plants.

Canines can stab and grip on to flesh.

Wolves eat meat. Which 2 types of teeth are important for this?

.............................................

and ............................................. .

Sheep eat grass. Which 2 types of teeth are important for this?

.............................................

and ............................................. .

6.  Draw lines to match the **animals** with the sets of **teeth** that you think they will have.

lion

rabbit

human

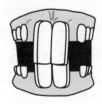

On the sets of teeth above, **colour in** the ones that will
help the animal **cut** or **tear** their food.

## INVESTIGATE

*Think about the following five animals — a goat, a tiger, a gorilla, a hamster and a badger.*
*Write down what you think they eat. Look in a book or online if you're unsure. Do you*
*think they eat meat, plants or both? Which teeth are the most important to each animal?*

*Section 2 — Teeth*

# Looking After Your Teeth

*Things that we <u>eat</u> or <u>drink</u> can be <u>bad</u> for our teeth. Luckily there are things we can do to <u>look after</u> our teeth and stop them getting <u>damaged.</u> That's what this mini-project is all about.*

You're going to study what happens to **egg shells** when you put them in different liquids. Egg shells are made of a similar material to **teeth**, so will react to the liquids in a similar way.

> ### Method:
> 1. Get 6 glasses and put some pieces of egg shell in each glass.
> 2. Fill each glass about half full with one of the following liquids
>    — cola, milk, fruit juice, water and vinegar.
> 3. Leave the glasses for 5 days.
> 4. After 5 days, take the egg shells out of the glasses. Dry them carefully with paper towels and record your results in the table below.

1. In order to find out how bad the liquid is for teeth, what will you need to **record** in the experiment? Tick (✔) the correct box.

   ☐ What happens to the egg shells.     ☐ What happens to the glass.     ☐ What happens to the liquid.

2. Write down what the **egg shells** looked like at the end of the experiment. I've put a few ideas of words you could use down the right-hand side of the table. There are some spare results at the bottom of page 11 if you didn't manage to do the experiment.

| Liquid | What did the egg shells look like after 5 days? |
|---|---|
| Cola | |
| Milk | |
| Fruit Juice | |
| Water | |
| Vinegar | |

*no change*

*brown*

*yellow*

*stained*

*soft*

*rough*

*smaller*

*holes*

*white*

*hard*

     *© CGP — not to be photocopied*

# Looking After Your Teeth

3.  Which liquids **did not** damage the egg shells?

    ..................................................................................................................

4.  Which liquids **did** damage the egg shells?

    ..................................................................................................................

5.  The table below shows whether there were high or low levels
    of **acid** and **sugar** in the different liquids.

    | Liquid | Level of acid | Level of sugar |
    |--------|---------------|----------------|
    | Cola | High | High |
    | Milk | Very Low | Low |
    | Fruit Juice | Very High | Very High |
    | Water | None | None |
    | Vinegar | Very High | None |

    Which liquids contained lots of **sugar**?

    ...........................................................................

    ...........................................................................

    Which liquids contained lots of **acid**?

    ...........................................................................

    ...........................................................................

6.  Use your answers to Q4 and Q5 to fill in the gaps in the sentences below.
    Use words from the tooth.

    The tooth was damaged by liquids that contained a

    lot of ............................. or were ............................. .

    The teeth that were left in sugary liquids or

    liquids ............................. in acid, changed .............................

    and developed ............................. .

    This experiment shows sugar and acid are ............................. for your teeth.

© CGP — not to be photocopied

# MINI-PROJECT

# *Looking After Your Teeth*

Below is a section from a dentist's website.
Use this to help you answer **Q7** to **Q9**.

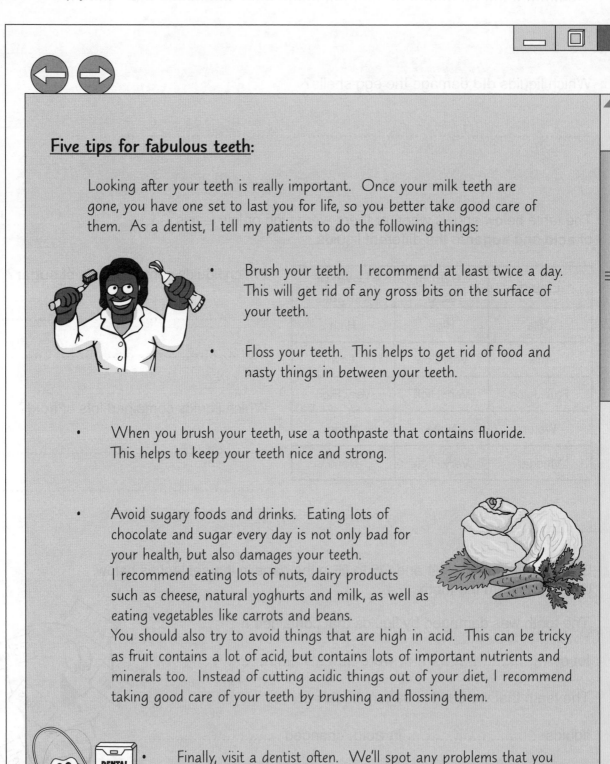

## Five tips for fabulous teeth:

Looking after your teeth is really important.  Once your milk teeth are gone, you have one set to last you for life, so you better take good care of them.  As a dentist, I tell my patients to do the following things:

- Brush your teeth.  I recommend at least twice a day. This will get rid of any gross bits on the surface of your teeth.

- Floss your teeth.  This helps to get rid of food and nasty things in between your teeth.

- When you brush your teeth, use a toothpaste that contains fluoride. This helps to keep your teeth nice and strong.

- Avoid sugary foods and drinks.  Eating lots of chocolate and sugar every day is not only bad for your health, but also damages your teeth. I recommend eating lots of nuts, dairy products such as cheese, natural yoghurts and milk, as well as eating vegetables like carrots and beans. You should also try to avoid things that are high in acid.  This can be tricky as fruit contains a lot of acid, but contains lots of important nutrients and minerals too.  Instead of cutting acidic things out of your diet, I recommend taking good care of your teeth by brushing and flossing them.

- Finally, visit a dentist often.  We'll spot any problems that you may have and make sure they're sorted out.

                    *© CGP — not to be photocopied*

# Answers to Y4 'Teeth, Digestion and Food Chains'

toothpaste that contains fluoride. 4. Avoid sugary foods and drinks. 5. Visit a dentist often.

8. Any three from: nuts, cheese, natural yoghurts, milk, carrots, beans. Any sensible suggestion of a dairy product or vegetable is also okay.

9. These pictures should be crossed out: cake, doughnuts, cola, chocolate, sweets and ice cream.

## Section 3 — Food Chains

### Page 14 — What Animals Eat

1. rabbit
2. grass, lettuce
3. vole, sparrow

### Page 15 — Predators and Prey

1. A. blackbird, B. fox, C. heron, D. spider
2.

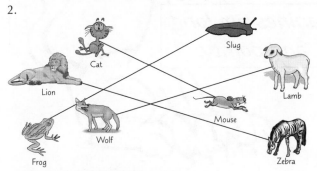

### Page 16 — Producers

1. producers, make, food
2. All producers are plants — ✔
   All plants are predators — ✘
   Some animals are producers — ✘
   Plants make their own food — ✔
3. The following things should be circled: a cactus, a daffodil, a tree, grass.

### Pages 17-19 — Food Chains

1.

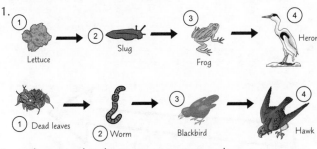

2. plant ➝ beetle ➝ mouse ➝ owl
   beetle and mouse
3. The pictures should be drawn out in this order:
   dandelion ➝ rabbit ➝ fox
   plant ➝ bugs ➝ minnows ➝ otter
   minnows
4. plant/leaf
5. trees
   ladybird, blackbird and cat.
6. The grass should be coloured in green, the mouse should be coloured in red and the owl should be coloured in blue.

### Pages 20-22 — Studying Food Chains

1. This will depend on the habitat you chose. The picture should include a few plants which are labelled.
2. These should be circled: The different animals in the habitat. What plants are in the habitat. What the animals in the habitat eat.
3. It depends on your results. Using the spare results, the table will look like this:

| Plants | Animals |
|---|---|
| rushes, algae, water lily, duckweed, | pond snail, water shrew, newt, duck, fly, worm, frog, heron, perch, mayfly |

4. It depends on your results. For the spare results your answer should look like this:

From top to bottom: true, true, false.

5. It depends on your results, but your food chain should follow this layout:
   Producer ➝ Prey ➝ Predator. Here are two examples you could get from the spare data:
   leaves ➝ worm ➝ newt
   algae ➝ pond snail ➝ frog

## Mixed Questions — pages 23-25

1. These should be ticked: teeth, tongue.
2.

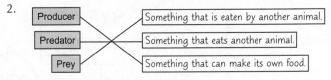

3.

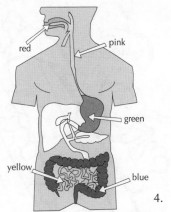

4. mouse
   palm tree

5. These should be circled: Floss your teeth. Use a toothpaste that contains fluoride. Eat less sugary and acidic foods. Brush your teeth twice a day.
6. From left to right: canine, incisor, molar.
7. wolf, shark, lion, cat
8. Pond weed ➝ pond snail ➝ minnow ➝ perch
9. molars, incisors, canines, canines, incisors
10. mouth, oesophagus, churned up, small, bloodstream, large

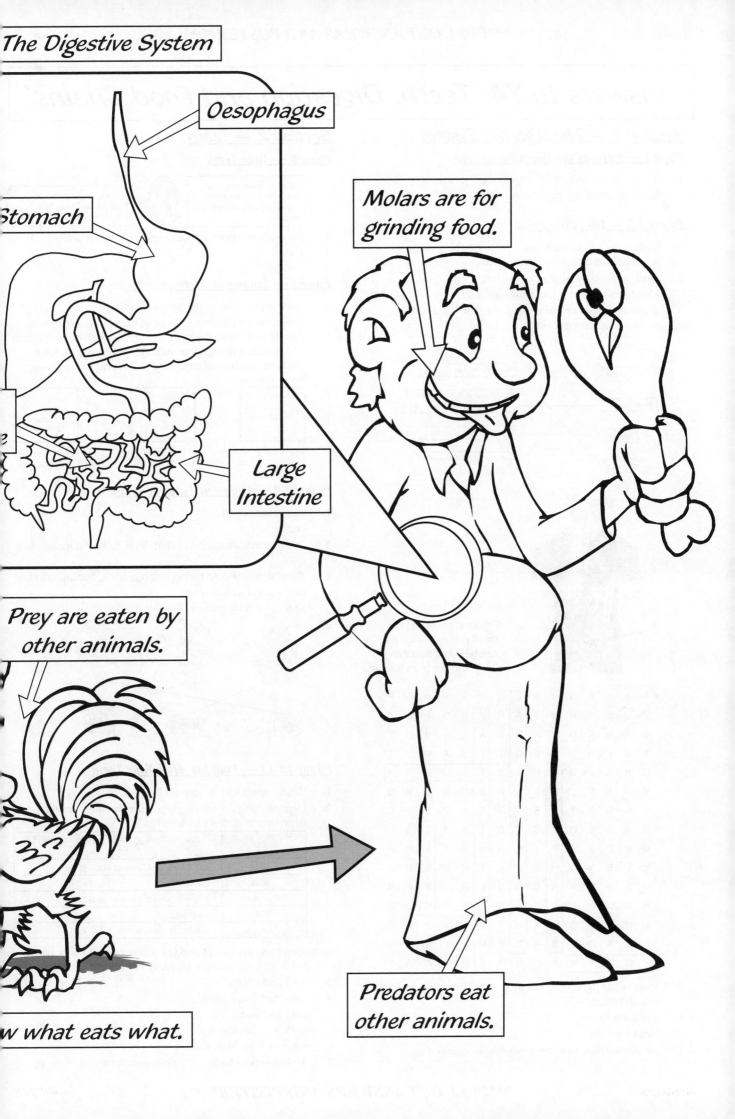

# Answers to Y4 'Teeth, Digestion and Food Chains'

## Section 1 — The Digestive System

### Page 1 — Parts of the Digestive System

1. 1. mouth,  2. tongue,  3. oesophagus,  4. stomach,
   5. small intestine,  6. large intestine

### Pages 2-5 — Digesting Food

1. 1. mouth,  2. oesophagus,  3. stomach,
   4. small intestine,  5. large intestine

2. Teeth and tongue should be circled.
   Heart should have a cross through it.

3. These words should be crossed out: air, lightly grilled,
   stomach, oesophagus, larger.

4.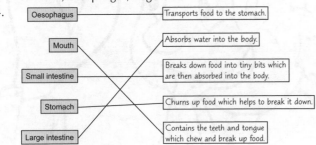

   | Oesophagus | Transports food to the stomach. |
   | Mouth | Absorbs water into the body. |
   | Small intestine | Breaks down food into tiny bits which are then absorbed into the body. |
   | Stomach | Churns up food which helps to break it down. |
   | Large intestine | Contains the teeth and tongue which chew and break up food. |

5.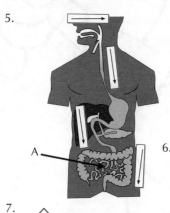

   A

6. The food needs to be in small pieces so that it can be taken into the body and the bloodstream.

7. 

| T | A | B | F | Q | U | A | L | E | R | T | M | A | Q | F |
|---|---|---|---|---|---|---|---|---|---|---|---|---|---|---|
| V | O | B | R | H | U | B | A | R | E | P | O | L | L | P |
| C | A | N | R | H | O | R | R | S | N | E | I | N | D | Y |
| Y | I | L | G | U | L | E | G | L | I | J | A | M | U | T |
| U | H | A | X | U | O | E | E | S | T | O | M | A | C | H |
| M | I | A | V | L | E | S | I | R | S | G | S | B | V | Q |
| Y | C | G | P | T | S | S | N | T | E | A | P | E | E | C |
| U | N | A | E | O | O | C | T | S | T | A | J | T | Q | U |
| M | I | C | H | E | P | I | E | N | N | E | A | E | P | P |
| Y | L | E | N | O | H | E | S | L | I | G | R | E | A | P |
| U | E | F | L | A | A | O | T | E | L | R | J | T | I | N |
| M | N | G | L | E | G | B | I | E | L | L | R | H | O | C |
| L | K | M | O | D | U | A | N | T | A | Y | B | P | A | Q |
| V | B | X | G | G | S | A | E | E | M | B | L | S | T | O |
| M | O | U | T | H | A | C | H | I | S | N | T | E | S | T |

8. From left to right: large intestine, small intestine, stomach, mouth/tongue.

9. small intestine

10. large intestine

11. mouth, smaller, swallow, oesophagus, churned up

## Section 2 — Teeth

### Page 6 — Your Teeth

1.

   Teeth are **white** and very **hard**. They are used to **break** up food and they help us to **eat**.

   These are the **gums**. They are soft and pink. They help to **hold** the teeth in place.

2. Depends on which of your teeth have fallen out.

3. Milk

### Page 7 — Shapes of Teeth

1. From left to right: molar, incisor, canine.

2. These are my pictures. Yours can be a bit different — as long as they show the shapes of the teeth. It doesn't matter which type is drawn in which box. You may also have different numbers of teeth in your top and bottom jaws. That's fine too.

   2 in my bottom jaw.
   2 in my top jaw.

   4 in my bottom jaw.
   4 in my top jaw.

   4 in my bottom jaw.
   4 in my top jaw.

### Pages 8-9 — Different Types of Teeth

1. sharp, flat-edged

2. cutting

3. These words should be circled: long, pointy, gripping, tear, front.

4. These words should be circled: big, back, bumpy, grinding.

5. Wolves: canines, molars
   Sheep: incisors, molars

6.

### Pages 10-13 — Looking After Your Teeth

1. What happens to the egg shells.

2. Depends on your results. If you use the spare results your table should look a bit like this:

| Liquid | What did the egg shells looked like after 5 days? |
|---|---|
| Cola | soft, holes, dark, almost black in colour |
| Milk | no change |
| Fruit Juice | soft, mouldy, light brown in colour |
| Water | no change |
| Vinegar | soft, holes, dark, almost black in colour |

The answers you get for Q3 and Q4 will depend on your results, but this is what your answers are likely to be:

3. milk and water.

4. cola, fruit juice, vinegar.

5. cola and fruit juice.
   cola, fruit juice and vinegar.

6. sugar, acidic, high, colour, holes, bad.

7. 1. Brush your teeth.  2. Floss your teeth.  3. Use a

# Looking After Your Teeth

7. What **five** things can you do to **protect** your teeth?

    1. ....................................................................................................

    2. ....................................................................................................

    3. ....................................................................................................

    4. ....................................................................................................

    5. ....................................................................................................

8. List **three** foods or drinks that are **good** for your teeth.

    ........................................................................................................

9. Put a cross (✗) through **six** foods that
   are the **most damaging** to your teeth.

   Hint — think about which foods are the most sugary.

EXTRA PROJECT

Get your teeth stuck into this extra project. Make a poster to
put in the dentist's office to tell patients how to look after their teeth. Include why it's
important that people look after their teeth and what happens if you don't look after
them. Use the results of your experiment on p10 and your answer to Q7 to help you.

# Section 3 — Food Chains

## What Animals Eat

*Different animals have different <u>diets</u>. Animals that eat <u>only meat</u> are called <u>carnivores</u> and animals that eat <u>only plants</u> are called <u>herbivores</u>. Some animals eat both <u>meat and plants</u>.*

1.   Write down which of these things a **fox** would eat.

Rabbit        Turnip            Cow

.......................................................

2.   Tick (✔) which **two** of these things a **rabbit** would eat.

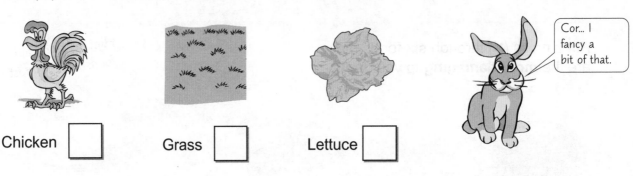

Chicken ☐        Grass ☐        Lettuce ☐

3.   Write down which **two** of these things a **cat** would eat.

Wood            Vole            Sparrow

.......................................................

## INVESTIGATE

- *Draw a table with two columns. Label one column 'Plants' and the other 'Meat'.*
- *Sort these animals into your table by deciding if they eat mainly plants or meat — a dog,*
- *a whale, an elephant, a crocodile, a turkey, a blackbird, a camel, a horse and a slug.*

# *Predators and Prey*

*An animal that eats another animal is called a <u>predator</u>.*
*The animal that gets eaten is called the <u>prey</u>.*

1.    Here are some pairs of predators and their prey.
      For each pair, write down which one is the **predator**.

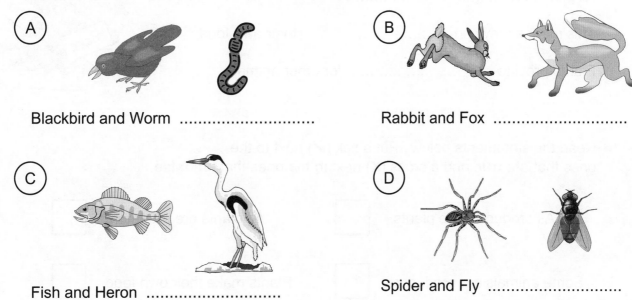

Blackbird and Worm ............................

Rabbit and Fox ............................

Fish and Heron ............................

Spider and Fly ............................

2.    Here is a group of **predators** and a group of **prey**.
      Draw a line between each of the predators and its prey.

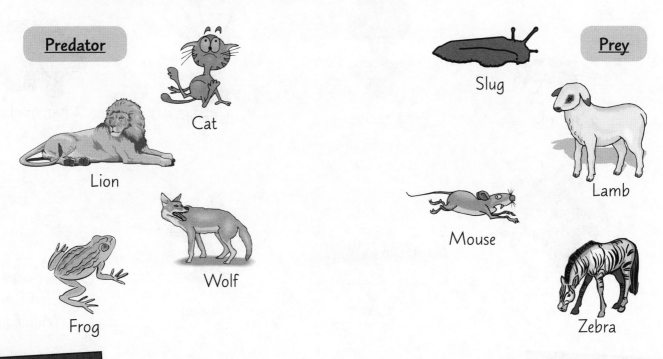

---

*INVESTIGATE* • • • • • • • • • • • • • • • • • • • • • • • • • • • • • • • •

*The following five animals are predators — a polar bear, a leopard, an eagle, a shark*
*and a badger. Can you think of two different prey for each of these predators?*
• • • • • • • • • • • • • • • • • • • • • • • • • • • • • • • • • • • • • • • • • •

© CGP — not to be photocopied                                          *Section 3 — Food Chains*

# Producers

*Plants __produce__ (make) their __own food__.  So they're called __producers__.*

1.  Use words from the tree on the left to complete the sentences below.

    All plants are ................................. .

    This means they can ................................. their own food.

    Plants provide ................................. for other animals.

2.  Read the statements below.  Put a tick (✔) next to the
    ones that are **true** and a cross (✗) next to the ones that are **false**.

    All producers are plants. ☐         All plants are predators. ☐

    Some animals are producers. ☐         Plants make their own food. ☐

3.  (Circle) the things below which are **producers**.

    a fly          a cactus          a daffodil          a hippopotamus

    a tree          grass          a dog          Chef Pierre Manifique

## INVESTIGATE

• *Draw and label pictures of four producers (that aren't in question 3).  Write the name of*
• *something that eats each of these producers next to their picture.*

          © CGP — not to be photocopied

# Food Chains

*A <u>food chain</u> shows what eats what. Almost all food chains start with a <u>plant</u>.*
*Arrows in food chains point from each organism <u>towards</u> the animal that eats it.*

1.  Fill in the **arrows** for these food chains. Follow the example.

2.  Here is a food chain with the organisms in the wrong order.
    Write their names in the **right order** in the spaces between the arrows.

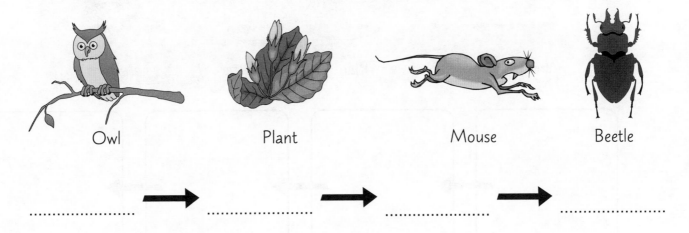

.....................  ➡  ....................  ➡  ....................  ➡  ....................

In the food chain above, which **two** things are **prey**?

1. ..............................................    2. ..............................................

© CGP — not to be photocopied

# Food Chains

3.  Make a **food chain** for each of these sets of organisms.
    Draw one organism in each box.

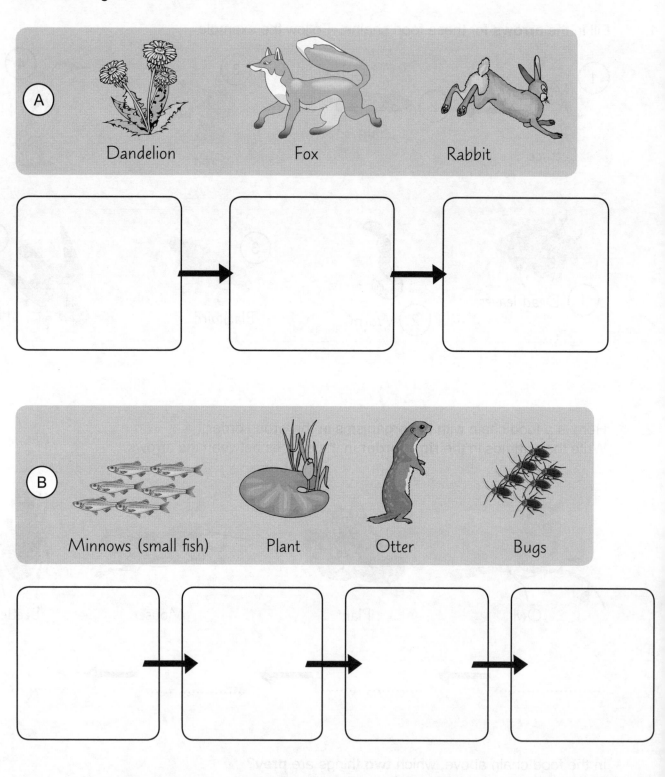

Which of the animals above is **both** a **predator** and **prey**?

..............................................................................................

*© CGP — not to be photocopied*

# Food Chains

4.  Most food chains start with a green plant. Fill in the **first organism** in this food chain (the caterpillar might give you a clue).

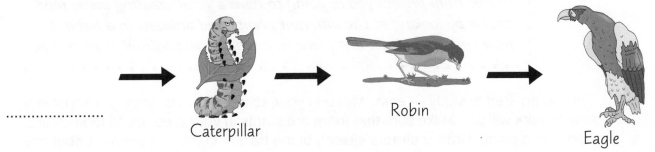

..................... Caterpillar Robin Eagle

5.  Use the **food chain** below to answer the following questions.

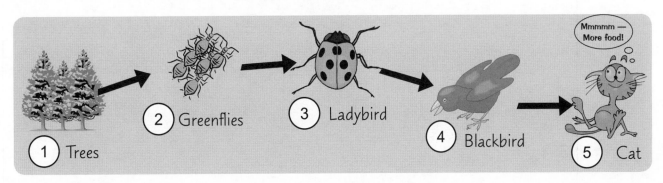

1 Trees    2 Greenflies    3 Ladybird    4 Blackbird    5 Cat    Mmmmm — More food!

Which organism in the food chain is a **producer**?

.................................................................................

Which organisms in the food chain are **predators**?

.................................................................................

*Organism is just another word for a living thing.*

6.  Look at the food chain below. Colour the **producer** in **green**, colour the **predator** in **blue**, and colour the **prey** in **red**.

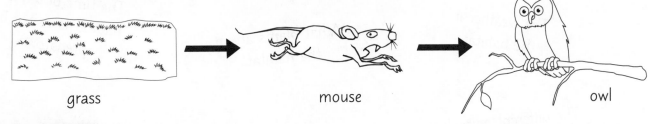

grass    mouse    owl

### INVESTIGATE

- Draw out one food chain that you might find in an ocean, one that you might find in a jungle and one you might find in a desert. Make sure your food chains have at least one producer, one prey and one predator. Label each organism in your food chain.

© CGP — not to be photocopied    *Section 3 — Food Chains*

# Studying Food Chains

*In this mini-project you're going to have a go at creating some food chains by looking at the different plants and animals in a habitat near you. (A habitat is a place where a specific animal or plant lives.)*

1. Choose an area to study — somewhere in your school grounds, your garden or in a nearby park will do. Make sure that there are plants in your area, as all food chains start with a plant. Draw a **simple sketch** of the habitat in the box below. **Label** any features in it that you think are important, such as a pond or different plants.

2. Circle the things you will need to **look at** to be able to work out the **food chains** in the habitat you've chosen.

The weather in the habitat.

What plants are in the habitat.

The time of day the habitat is visited by predators.

The different animals in the habitat.

What the animals in the habitat eat.

Whether the animals in the habitat wear socks.

*© CGP — not to be photocopied*

# Studying Food Chains

3. Study the habitat and fill in the table below with all the **plants** and **animals** that you see.

You may need to go back to the habitat at different times to see all the animals that visit it. You may need a teacher or adult to help you identify some of them.

| Plants | Animals |
|---|---|
| ................................................. | ................................................. |
| ................................................. | ................................................. |
| ................................................. | ................................................. |
| ................................................. | ................................................. |
| ................................................. | ................................................. |

If you can't do this experiment yourself, there are some spare results at the bottom of this page.

4. Are the animals and plants in your table **producers**, **prey** or **predators**? Sort them into the correct category by writing them in the bubbles below.

*Watch out — some of your animals may fit into more than one category.*

( **Producer** )     ( **Prey** )     ( **Predator** )

Use your answers above to decide whether the following statements are **true** or **false**. Put a tick (✔) in the correct column.

|  | True | False |
|---|---|---|
| All of the producers are plants. | ☐ | ☐ |
| All of the predators are animals. | ☐ | ☐ |
| Some of the producers are also predators. | ☐ | ☐ |

Here are some spare results for you to use: animals and plants in my chosen habitat (a pond) — pond snail, water shrew, rushes, newt, duck, fly, worm, frog, water lily, duckweed, heron, perch, mayfly, algae.

# *Studying Food Chains*

5. Use your answer to question 4 to help you make two food chains for the habitat.

Draw **pictures** of the **animals** and **plants** that you're using in the boxes below and draw arrows between them.

Remember — arrows go from the animal that is eaten to the animal that eats it.

.................................     .................................     .................................

.................................     .................................     .................................

Write the **name** of each animal or plant on the dotted lines below each box.

*EXTRA PROJECT*

*Choose one of the predators from the habitat and do some research to find out all of the different things it eats. You can use your results from this mini-project to help you, as well as books and the Internet. Show what you've found out on a poster by drawing and labelling pictures of your predator and its different prey.*

# Mixed Questions

*Get your teeth stuck into these questions all about the <u>digestive</u> <u>system</u>, <u>teeth</u> and <u>food chains</u>. Bon appétit...*

1.  Tick (✔) the **two** parts of the body that are in the **mouth**.

    Teeth ☐                     Large intestine ☐

    Small intestine ☐           Tongue ☐

    Oesophagus ☐                Lungs ☐

2.  Use lines to match the words on the left with the correct description on the right.

    | Producer | | Something that is eaten by another animal. |

    | Predator | | Something that eats another animal. |

    | Prey | | Something that can make its own food. |

3.  The picture on the right shows the digestive system.
    **Colour** the different parts in the following way:

    Colour the mouth in red.

    Colour the large intestine in blue.

    Colour the stomach in green.

    Colour the small intestine in yellow.

    Colour the oesophagus in pink.

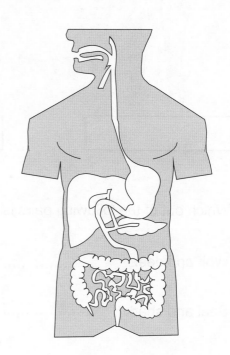

© CGP — not to be photocopied                                    *Mixed Questions*

# Mixed Questions

4.  Look at the organisms below then answer the questions.

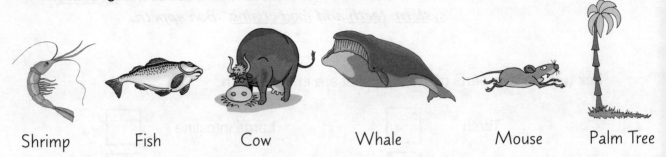

| Shrimp | Fish | Cow | Whale | Mouse | Palm Tree |

Which of the organisms would be **prey** for a **fox**? ............................... .

Which of these organisms is a **producer**? ........................... .

5.  (Circle) **four** things that you can do to protect your teeth.

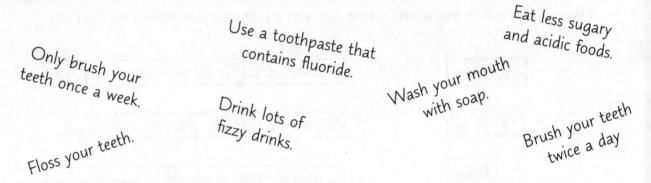

Only brush your teeth once a week.

Use a toothpaste that contains fluoride.

Eat less sugary and acidic foods.

Floss your teeth.

Drink lots of fizzy drinks.

Wash your mouth with soap.

Brush your teeth twice a day

6.  Write the correct tooth name under each picture — **incisor**, **canine** or **molar**.

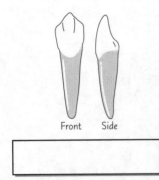

Front    Side

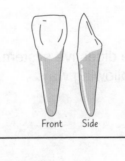

Front    Side

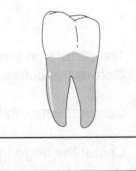

7.  Which out of the following pairs is the **predator**?

Wolf and deer          .........................          Lion and antelope          .........................

Seal and shark          .........................          Sparrow and cat          .........................

          © CGP — not to be photocopied

# Mixed Questions

8. This is a food chain with the organisms in the **wrong** order.
Write their names in the **right** order in the spaces between the arrows.

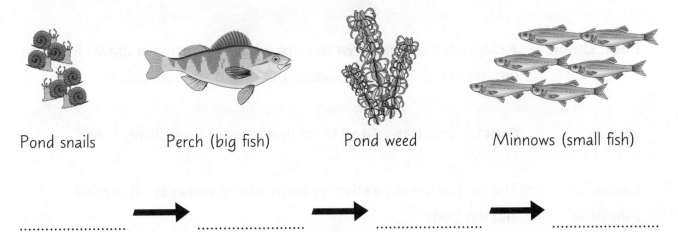

Pond snails          Perch (big fish)          Pond weed          Minnows (small fish)

....................... ➡ ....................... ➡ ....................... ➡ .......................

9. Write in **incisors**, **canines** or **molars** to finish off these sentences.

................................... are good for grinding up food.

................................... are good for cutting through plants.

................................... can stab and grip on to meat.

Meat eaters have very large ................................... .

Animals that eat plants have large ................................... .

10. Use the words on the right to fill in the gaps in the sentences below.

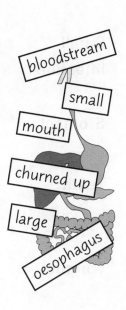

Food is taken into the body at the ................................... and

travels down the ................................... to the stomach.

In the stomach, the food is ................................... .

Food then passes to the ................................... intestine

where it is absorbed into the ................................... .

The last place it reaches is the ................................... intestine.

bloodstream

small

mouth

churned up

large

oesophagus

© CGP — not to be photocopied

# Glossary

| | |
|---|---|
| **Canine** | A **long** and **pointy** tooth used for **gripping** and **tearing food**. |
| **Food Chain** | A diagram that shows **what eats what**. An arrow is drawn from the organism that is eaten towards the organism that eats it. |
| **Incisor** | A **sharp** and **flat-edged** tooth that is used for **cutting food**. |
| **Large Intestine** | The part of the **digestive system** where **water** is **absorbed** into the body. |
| **Molar** | A **large** tooth with a **bumpy** surface that is used for **grinding up** food. |
| **Mouth** | The part of the **digestive system** that contains the **teeth** and **tongue**. |
| **Oesophagus** | The **pipe** in the **digestive system** that transports food to the **stomach**. |
| **Predator** | An animal that kills and **eats another animal**. |
| **Prey** | An animal that is **eaten by** another animal. |
| **Producer** | An organism that **produces** (makes) its own **food**. Always a **plant**. |
| **Small Intestine** | The part of the **digestive system** where food is **absorbed** into the **bloodstream**. |
| **Stomach** | The part of the **digestive system** where food is **churned up**. |
| **Teeth** | Part of the **digestive system**. The teeth are in the **mouth**. They **chew** and **break up** food. |
| **Tongue** | Part of the **digestive system**. The tongue is in the **mouth**. It helps to **chew**, **break up** and **swallow** food. |

 © *CGP — not to be photocopied*